Sight Word Tales™

don't   be
there   under

Don't Be Afraid, Monster

by Maria Fleming
illustrated by Mike Moran

W9-ATK-683

COMPLIMENTS OF
PORTAGE TWP SCHOOLS
TITLE I

SCHOLASTIC INC.

New York • Toronto • London • Auckland • Sydney
Mexico City • New Delhi • Hong Kong • Buenos Aires

Designed by Maria Lilja
ISBN-13: 978-0-545-01652-0 • ISBN-10: 0-545-01652-5
Copyright © 2007 by Scholastic Inc.
All rights reserved. Printed in China.

First printing, November 2007

12 11 10 9 8 7 6 5 4 3 2 1   7 8 9 10 11 12/0

Don't be afraid, Monster.

There is nothing scary **under** the blanket.

Don't be afraid, Monster.

There is nothing scary **under** the desk.

Don't be afraid, Monster.

There is nothing scary **under** the coat.

Don't be afraid, Monster.

There is nothing scary **under** the towel.

Don't be afraid, Monster.

There is nothing scary **under** the bed.

Time to go to sleep, Monster.

Sweet dreams **under there**!

Sight Word Review

Do you know the four sight words in this book? Read aloud the word on each pillow.

don't

there

under

be

there

don't

be

under

14

Sight Word Fill-ins

Listen to the sentences. Then choose a sight word from the box to fill in each blank.

> **Word Box**   **don't**   **be**   **there**   **under**

1 You can _____ so silly!

2 They _____ want to go.

3 The crayons are over _____.

4 My shoe was _____ the bed.

5 We _____ need our coats today.

6 Are _____ any more apples?

7 The ball rolled _____ the bush.

8 I have to _____ home by noon.

Sight Word Cheers

Celebrate the new sight words you learned by saying these four short cheers.

D-o-n'-t! Give a yell!
What do these four letters spell?
A sight word that we all know well —
Don't, don't, don't!

B-e! Give a yell!
What do these two letters spell?
A sight word that we all know well —
Be, be, be!

T-h-e-r-e! Give a yell!
What do these five letters spell?
A sight word that we all know well —
There, there, there!

U-n-d-e-r! Give a yell!
What do these five letters spell?
A sight word that we all know well —
Under, under, under!